JAMIE SMART'S

BUNNY vs MONKEY

THE ⚡IMPOSSIBLE⚡PIG!

4

5

WEENIE! JOIN OUR TEAM AND YOU CAN HAVE THIS BISCUIT! I'VE SAVED YOU TIME AND ALREADY LICKED THE CHOCOLATE OFF IT.

BLECK! NO!

PIG! WANT TO BE EVIL?

NOT AGAIN.

WHAT?

WHAT?

WHHHH-UT?

LE FOX! YOU WOULD BE PERFECT FOR OUR TEAM! YOU ALREADY HATE EVERYONE.

PAH! WHY WOULD I JOIN YOU?

YOU DISGUST ME. EVERYTHING YOU DO, EVERY THOUGHT YOU HAVE, IT SICKENS ME. WHEN YOU BREATHE I CAN HEAR IT AND IT MAKES ME RETCH. I WILL SPEND MY ENTIRE LIFE DESPISING YOUR EXISTENCE!

IF YOU WORK WITH US, SKUNKY WILL INVENT YOU SOMETHING.

WHAT?

ZEN IT IS A DEAL.

8

9

12

15

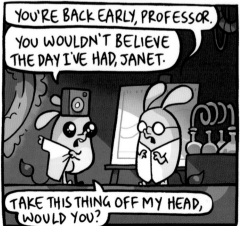

17

22

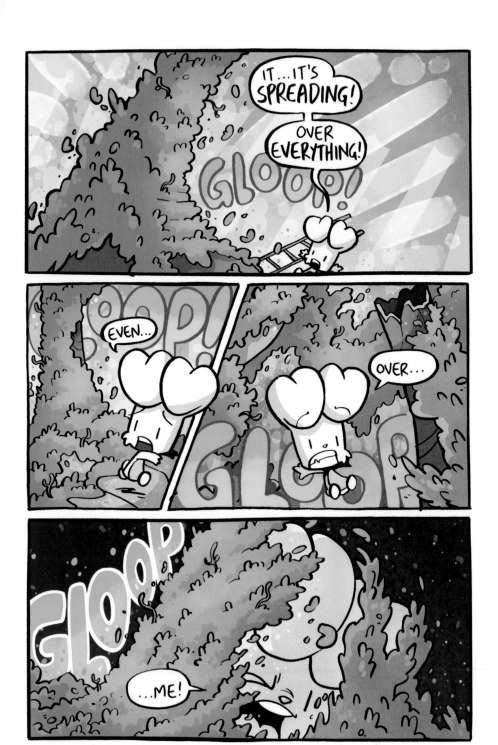

30

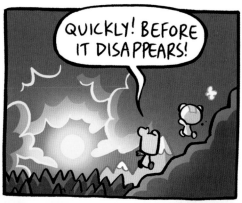

34

"WIPEY"

40

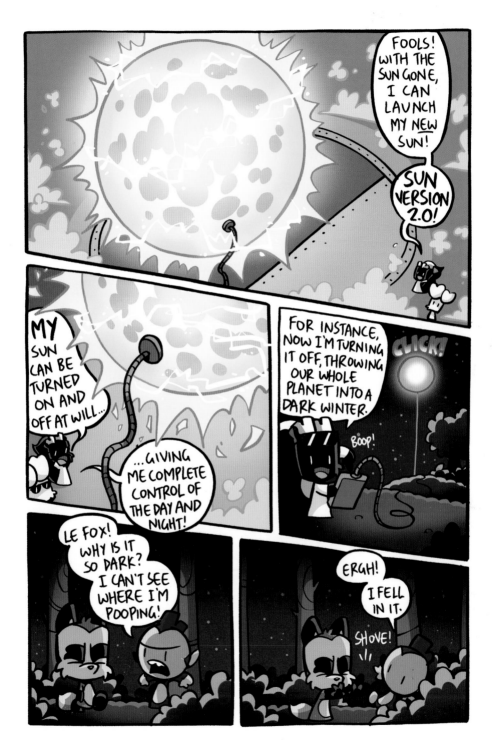

FOOLS! WITH THE SUN GONE, I CAN LAUNCH MY NEW SUN!

SUN VERSION 2.0!

MY SUN CAN BE TURNED ON AND OFF AT WILL...

...GIVING ME COMPLETE CONTROL OF THE DAY AND NIGHT!

FOR INSTANCE, NOW I'M TURNING IT OFF, THROWING OUR WHOLE PLANET INTO A DARK WINTER.

CLICK!

BOOP!

LE FOX! WHY IS IT SO DARK? I CAN'T SEE WHERE I'M POOPING!

ERGH! I FELL IN IT.

SHOVE!

'BODY SWAP'

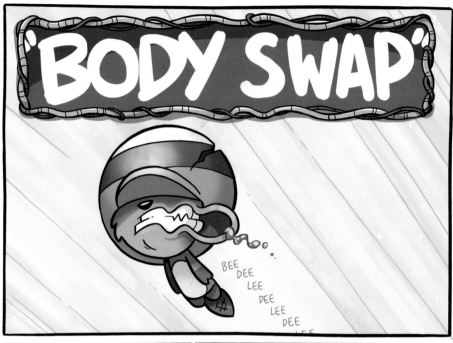

EXCELLENT WORK, ACTION BEAVER!

THAT'S THE 1,593RD TIME I'VE FIRED YOU INTO THE WALL, AND YET YOUR SKULL IS STILL COMPLETELY INTACT.

IF ONLY I COULD HARNESS YOUR POWER.

YOUR STRENGTH.

YOUR RESILIENCE.

48

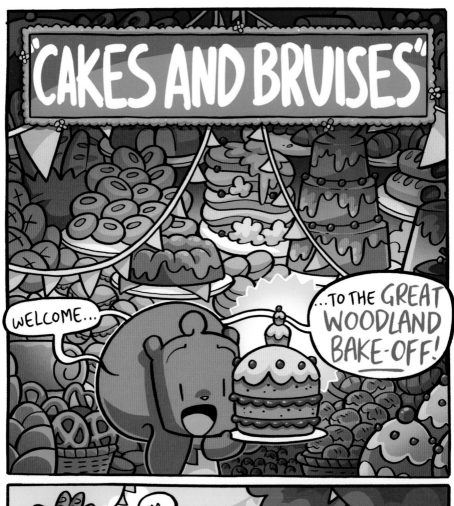

49

THE...THE **BAKING** CONTEST! I'VE BEEN PLANNING IT FOR MONTHS!

I ASKED PIG TO SEND EVERYONE INVITATIONS TO PARTICIPATE!

OH! I STILL HAVE THEM! WHAT DO YOU WANT ME TO DO WITH THEM?

BUT I'VE WORKED SO **HARD.** I'VE BAKED BROWNIES, BISCUITS, DOUGHNUTS, PANCAKES, PANINI, CROSTINI, BAGELS, NAANS, BLOOMERS, COBS, PLAITS AND STOTTIES, SCONES, GATEAUX, CHEESECAKES, SWISS ROLLS, BAUMKUCHENS AND BLONDIES.

FRRP!

AND THIS THING. WHATEVER IT IS.

WEENIE, IF IT MEANS SO MUCH TO YOU THEN WE'LL **ALL** COMPETE IN THE WOODLAND BAKE-OFF!

you **WILL?**

EVERYONE, -GET- BAKING!

YEEEP!

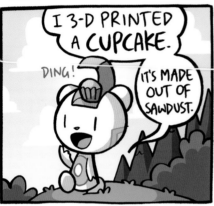

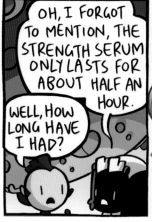

THIS IS A NEW START FOR ME. FROM NOW ON, I'M GOING TO BE ☆☆ GOOD! ☆☆

LOTS OF GOOD LATER...

PIG! ALLOW ME TO CARRY YOU!

WHEE!

I KNOW I SHOULD BE HAPPY THAT MONKEY'S BEING GOOD...

... BUT MY GOODNESS THESE WOODS ARE BORING NOW.

THINGS'LL SOON LIVEN UP AGAIN. I'VE FIXED MY OCTOBOT AFTER MONKEY CARELESSLY DROPPED IT ONTO HIS HEAD.

BWOO

LOOK, MONKEY! AN EVIL INVENTION! DOESN'T THAT MAKE YOU WANT TO CAUSE MAYHEM?

NOT REALLY...

AS A **GOOD MONKEY**, I'D FAR RATHER **DEFEAT** IT AND BRING A LASTING PEACE TO THE WOODS!

BLAAHGLE BLAHGLE BLAHG!

KICK KICK KICK

PEEE-YOOO

CRUMP!

I'VE CHANGED MY MIND. BEING GOOD IS BAD FOR MY HEALTH.

YAYYY!

57

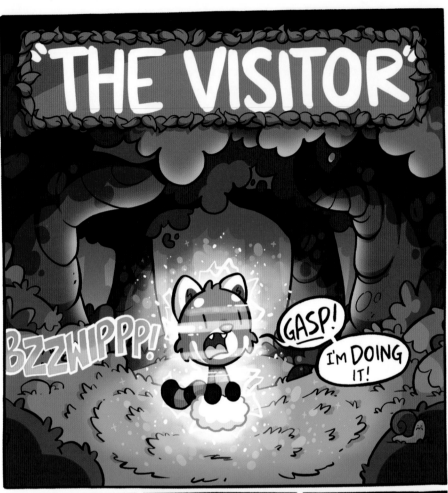

I FEEL ALL ...BUBBLY... IN MY TUMMY.

YOU DON'T HAVE A TUMMY ANY MORE, PIG! WE'VE BECOME PART OF THE ATMOSPHERE!

BUKAWK!!

IF WE CONCENTRATE, MAYBE WE CAN REFORM INTO OUR PHYSICAL BODIES.

BZZ WIP!

THERE! I DID IT!

NOW YOU, PIG!

PIG?

UMM. PIG?

NO, THIS IS RIDICULOUS. WHO ARE YOU REALLY?

I'M PIG! I TOLD YOU!

PROVE IT.

I WILL! WHAT DID PIG LIKE DOING? I MEAN... WHAT DO I LIKE DOING?

WELL...

THERE'S THIS WEIRD PATCH OF GROUND WHICH IS ALWAYS SQUELCHY. PIG LIKED POKING IT WITH A STICK.

FINE!

I'M DOING IT.

SQUELCH! SQUOCH!

I REMEMBER WHEN PIG ATE SEVENTEEN DOUGHNUTS BECAUSE HE KEPT FORGETTING THE PREVIOUS ONE HE'D EATEN.

THERE! GULP!

OH. THIS IS DISGUSTING.

AND, OF COURSE, PIG JUST LOVES DIGGING HOLES.

OKAY?

OKAY?

HMM. NO. NOT LIKE THAT.

RRGH! FOR GOODNESS' SAKE, I AM PIG. I AM.

PIG NEVER GOT ANGRY.

RRRGHH!

WHY WOULD I LIE ABOUT BEING PIG? BECAUSE I'M ACTUALLY A RED PANDA WHO ACCIDENTALLY BZZWIPPED THE REAL PIG INTO THE MOLECULAR STREAM?

WELL... WELL, THAT NEVER HAPPENED.

WHY WOULD YOU EVEN SUGGEST IT?

PIG WOULD HAVE CHASED THAT BUTTERFLY.

WHERE WOULD YOU EVEN FIND SUCH A THING?

SKUNKY! HE FOUND IT GROWING IN ONE OF HIS SANDWICHES.

AND NOW IT'S YOURS! BYE!

HYUK HYUK.

WHAT?

NO!

BUNNY, IT SMELLS LIKE POOEY SOCKS!

I KNOW! BUT WHAT CAN WE DO?

TEAM MEETING!

WHAT? I TOLD YOU, I'M PIG.

68

71

SO, AS A BACK-UP PLAN, I HAD SKUNKY FILL SOME OF THE BALLOONS...

...WITH COMPLIANCE GAS!!

BOOP!

POP!

POP!

I DON'T EVEN KNOW WHAT THAT WORD MEANS!

IT MEANS YOU'LL DO WHATEVER I SAY. NOW GO AND VOTE FOR ME AT THE POLLS!

☐ MONKEY
☐ SOMEONE ELSE

YES, MASTER, I WILL.

EXCITED SQUEALING!

SOME VOTING LATER...

LE FOX! YOU CAN COUNT THE VOTES SINCE YOU'RE IMPARTIAL.

I HATE EVERYONE.

THAT'S WHAT I SAID!

ZE WINNER IS... SIGH... MONKEY.

I WON! I WON!

OH NO! WHAT HAVE WE DONE?

73

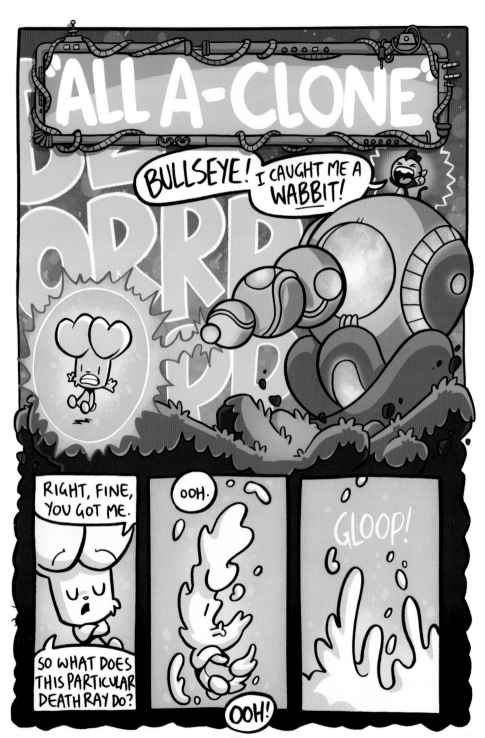

77

GO AND GET THE **VACUUM CLEANER.**

YOU'VE MADE A RIGHT MESS.

82

WHAT ARE YOU LOSERS DOING? DID YOU ALL FALL OVER?

WE'RE WATCHING THE CLOUDS, MONKEY!

SOMETIMES THEY LOOK LIKE THINGS!

LIKE THAT ONE! IT LOOKS LIKE YOUR FACE!

RRRGH! I'LL RUIN YOUR FUN—I'LL BUST THOSE CLOUDS APART WITH JUST THE POWER OF MY MIND!

RRGH! RRGH!

PFFT!

I...I DON'T THINK IT'S WORKING, MONKEY.

FINE. FINE. I'LL FIND A BETTER WAY TO DO IT.

SKUNKY! INVENT ME SOMETHING TO BUST THE CLOUDS UP!

CAN IT WAIT? I'M HAVING BRUNCH.

NO, I NEED IT NOW.

OH, HELLO, PIG.

HI!

HMM, WELL, I DO HAVE SOMETHING THAT NEEDS TESTING.

PROTOTYPES

HAR HAR HAR! LET'S SEE THOSE RUDE CLOUDS WITHSTAND THE POWER OF MY NEW PSYCHIC WEATHER CHANGER!

BWOOZUM!

OUR CLOUDS!

HE'S BUSTING THEM!

85

87

"POCKET PIG"

THURSDAY, AND QUITE A FEW OF THE WOODLAND ANIMALS ARE UNHAPPY...

TO BE HONEST, I DON'T KNOW WHAT WE'RE DOING. I JUST WANTED TO SET FIRE TO A BRANCH.

OH, HI, EVERYONE! I'M JUST PUTTING BUTTERFLIES UP MY NOSE, LIKE PIG DOES. DID.

SEEMS LIKE A THING HE'D HAVE DONE. I'D HAVE DONE. AM DOING.

YOU'RE NOT PIG AT ALL, YOU'RE AN IMPOSTER.

OHHHH YEAH, I CAN SEE IT NOW.

I.. I...

NNNN NNN NGG GGG GGG!

FINE! IT'S TRUE! MY NAME'S ACTUALLY LUCKY, AND IT'S MY FAULT PIG'S GONE, BUT I FELT REALLY GUILTY ABOUT IT SO I THOUGHT MAYBE I COULD PRETEND TO BE HIM BUT I DON'T EVEN LIKE BUTTERFLIES.

PIG NEVER PUT BUTTERFLIES UP HIS NOSE!

THEN WHY AM I DOING THIS?

BOO HOO HOO HOO!

92

JUST TELL US WHERE THE REAL PIG IS!

I...I DON'T KNOW! HE'S EVERYWHERE, FLOATING AROUND, HIS MOLECULES INTERMINGLING WITH OURS.

THAT DOESN'T SOUND LIKE PIG.

ASK SKUNKY, HE KNOWS!

OH, YOU GRASS.

YEAH, FINE, WHATEVER. I'VE KNOWN FOR AGES.

PIG HAS BEEN ABSORBED INTO THE MOLECULAR STREAM. IT'S MOST LIKELY IMPOSSIBLE TO BRING HIM BACK.

I DID, HOWEVER, FIND HIS FREQUENCY IN THE UNIVERSAL INTERFERENCE, AND CHANNELLED HIM INTO A ROBOT TEASMAID!

AND IT'S THAT SAME TECHNOLOGY I'VE ADAPTED TO TRANSFORM HIM INTO A POCKET PIG PET!

PIG?! IS THAT YOU?

THE WI-FI'S NOT GREAT OUT HERE, BUT HE SHOULD WORK OKAY.

94

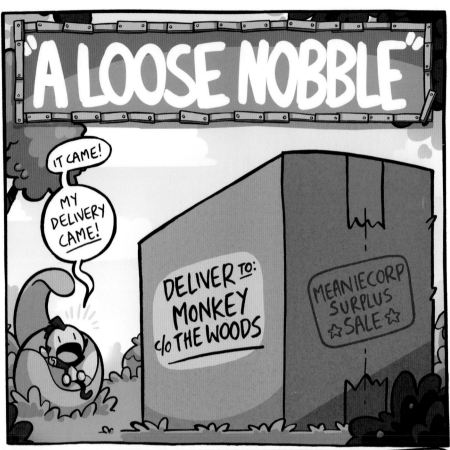

"LUCKY'S HOME"

LUCKY, AS THE NEWEST ADDITION TO THE WOODS, WE THOUGHT IT IMPORTANT YOU FEEL WELCOME!

SO WE ALL WORKED TOGETHER AND BUILT YOU A HOME!

GASP!

IT'S...

CRUMP

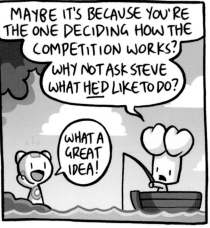

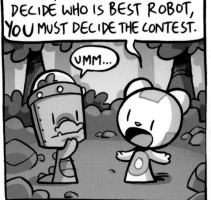

113

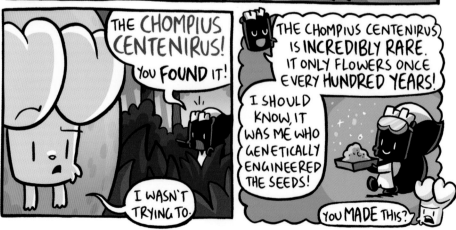

ANYWAY, BE CAREFUL WHERE YOU STEP. THERE COULD BE MORE SEEDS BENEATH YOUR FEET, WAITING TO STRIKE AT ANY TIME.

YOU'RE STANDING ON A LITERAL MINEFIELD!

ONLY THEY'RE NOT MINES.

AND THIS ISN'T A FIELD.

NAH, IT'S FINE. I'M SUPER FAST! I CAN ESCAPE ANYTHING!

WATCH ME.

CHOMP!

CHOMP! CHO

YOINK!

YOINK!

YOINK!

PUFF PUFF! THERE! SEE? NONE OF THEM CAME CLOSE!

CHOMP

OH, FAIR PLAY.

I WASN'T EXPECTING THAT.

117

"TIME AND AGAIN"

HAR HAR HAR... THE WOODS ARE ABLAZE AS LONG AS I...

...CAPTAIN EXPLOSIVES, AM ON THE LOOSE!

MONKEY! WHAT ON EARTH ARE YOU DOING?

NOT MONKEY! CAPTAIN EXPLOSIVES!

GIVE ME THAT SILLY HELMET.

OH, FINE. I AM MONKEY.

SNATCH!

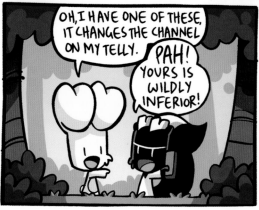

"THE SECOND PIGGING"

BUNNY.

HEY, BUNNY.

HELLO?

IT'S ME. SKUNKY. I'M TALKING TO YOU TELEPATHICALLY.

I IMPLANTED A PSYCHIC CHIP IN MY SKULL SOME YEARS AGO.

SO CAN YOU READ OUR MINDS?

PROBABLY.

GO ON THEN.

READ ACTION BEAVER'S MIND.

ALL I CAN HEAR IS THE SOUND OF A BROKEN TOILET.

GASP!

YOU CAN DO IT!

CAN YOU TWO STOP YAPPING? I'M TRYING TO FART.

OH.

YEAH.

I IMPLANTED A CHIP IN MONKEY'S SKULL TOO.

BUT IT DOESN'T MATTER, WE NEED TO COME UP WITH A WAY TO UNFREEZE TIME!

I KNOW A REALLY ANNOYING SONG.

MONKEY, NO.

I'M A MONKEY, I'M A MONKEY, I'M A MONKEY, I'M A MONKEY.

MONKEY, STOP IT.

CHORUS! MONKEY MONKEY MONKEY MONKEY MONKEY!

129

"HAIRY NEARLY"

I HAVE CRAWLED ACROSS MOUNTAINS...

THROUGH BROWN SQUELCHY THINGS...

INTO CAVES... OUT OF CAVES...

...BACK INTO CAVES BECAUSE I LEFT MY SANDWICH IN THERE...

...ALL TO FIND MY WAY BACK TO YOU...

...MY FRIENDS.

HMM, SKUNKY MUST HAVE FROZEN TIME USING A REMOTE CONTROL POWERED BY TIME CRYSTALS.

AT A GUESS.

MONKEYMONKEY MONK— OH, AM I SINGING THIS OUT LOUD?

WE'RE UNFROZEN!

YES, AND IT WAS ALL THANKS TO M—

DID EVERYONE ELSE SEE PIG?!

I DID!

HE WAS A HUGE FLOATING HEAD!

HE HAD LONG HAIR AND A BEARD!

IT WAS A MIRACLE!

CAN I FINISH MY SONG?

AND LOOK! ONE OF HIS LUSTROUS BEARD HAIRS FELL OUT!

GAAASP!

PIG HAIR EMITS A **UNIQUE DNA SIGNAL!** IF I CAN MANIPULATE IT, I MIGHT BE ABLE...

...TO BRING **PIG BACK!**

OH. YAY.

HOW EXCITING! I CAN'T WAIT TO SEE HIM AGAIN!

IS EVERYONE READY TO SEE A GIANT FLOATING PIG HEAD WITH A BEARD?

I WAS BORN READY FOR THAT!

BOOP! BWOOOOO!

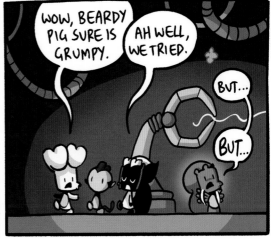

ZOMBIES!

MONKEY! IT'S 2 A.M.! WHAT ON EARTH ARE YOU DOING?

CLUCK CLUCK!

OH. SORRY.

AM I DOING IT AGAIN?

EVER SINCE I WALKED IN ON SKUNKY TRYING TO REANIMATE A CHICKEN, I'VE BEEN HAVING THESE FUNNY SPELLS. ALMOST AS IF...

POKE!

...YOU'VE BEEN POSSESSED BY THE SPIRIT OF A CHICKEN?

BUKAWK!!

I DUNNO, MAYBE.

WELL, IF SKUNKY CAUSED THIS, I'M SURE HE CAN...

SQUAWK!

OW!

OW!

SQUAWK!

GET OFF!

SQUAWK!

GET OFF ME!

137

BBBBZZZZZZ ZZZZZZZZ!!

140

'TURTLE-Y RIDICULOUS'

BUT **TURTLE ANNIHILATION** WORKS A LOT BETTER! IT'S LIKE **TOTAL** ANNIHILATION, BUT WITH THE WORD **TURTLE** INSTEAD.

NO, NO, I GET IT.

I CAN'T SAY TORTOISE-AL ANNIHILATION.

I'M JUST SAYING, IT'S AN IMPORTANT DISTINCTION.

FINE. FINE.

ONWARDS, DESTRUCTIVE BEAST OF UNDETERMINED NAME!

TEAR THESE WOODS APART BENEATH YOUR RAMPAGING FEET!

TRUDGE.

TRUDGE.

I'M STARTING TO THINK THIS WAS A RUBBISH INVENTION.

142

YOU DO!

I DON'T.

YOU DO!

I DON'T.

YOU DO!

I ASSURE YOU, I DON'T.

HOWEVER, I MIGHT BE ABLE TO HELP. YOU SEE, IN FOLKLORE, OWLS ARE A **PORTENT** OF **DOOM**!

OOH! I LIKE DOOM!

SO LET'S SEE IF I CAN CONNECT WITH NATURE, AND ATTUNE MYSELF MENTALLY WITH THE OWLS...

BWOOO

A GREAT FOE IS COMING. THEY WILL **VANQUISH YOUR SCHEMES,** AND **GRIND YOUR BONES TO DUST.**

WHAT?

I'LL BET IT'S **BUNNY**, HE'S ALWAYS HAD IT IN FOR ME.

WELL.

MAYBE I'LL JUST GO AND **VANQUISH HIM FIRST.**

150

LOOK! NOW I'M THIS GOPHER!

PLLPPP!!

I KNOW, ISN'T IT.

I TRIED TO COMMUNICATE WITH YOUR FRIENDS, BUT THEIR BRAINS WERE TOO PRIMITIVE TO UNDERSTAND MY MESSAGE.

BZZZ!

GRRPP!

PERHAPS YOU COULD CONVEY MY MESSAGE FOR ME?

TELL THEM I AM HERE, AMONGST YOU ALL, AND A GREAT LOVE SHALL BE BLESSED UPON THIS WORLD.

ALSO...

ACTION BEAVER!

YOU SURVIVED!

EXPERIMENT #5973 WAS A SUCCESS!

BUT...HE BLEW UP!

THAT WAS THE POINT OF EXPERIMENT #5973.

OHHH.

153

GRUARGHH! THE FLAME KING HAS ARRIVED TO TOAST YOU ALL UP A BIT!

OH, ALSO HE'S MASSIVE NOW.

NO FAIR, MONKEY. YOU'RE RUINING MY BIG REVEAL!

GRARGLE! GOOD!

WITH MY FIERY BURPS I CAN BLAST THROUGH YOUR WINTER!

ONCE THE FIRE HAS DIED DOWN, THE COLD THRIVES!

GETTOFF! NYARGH!

HEY, SKUNKY, MAYBE STOP MAKING THESE BODYSUITS?

UM...

TOO LATE.

OH, FOR GOODNESS' SAKE.

158

HEY, SKUNKY! IF I CAN KISS MY OWN BUTT, YOU HAVE TO LEND ME YOUR BRAIN!

WHAT?

MWAHH!

SO C'MON THEN, BUNNY! YOU AND ME, ON THE INTELLECTUAL PLAYING FIELDS...

UMM...

WINNER GETS THE WOODS!

STANDBY

ON

FLICK!

OR ARE YOU... CHICKEN?

101 VERY HARD QUESTIONS ACTUALLY.

WELL, LET'S SEE, HOW HARD CAN THIS BE...

FINISHED!

GAAAASP! YOU GOT ALL THE QUESTIONS RIGHT, TOO!

WIIINNER!

MAL

43 × 892 = 38,356

CAPITAL CITY OF BAHAMAS: Nassau

SKUNKY! TAKE YOUR BRAIN BACK AND COME UP WITH A WAY TO KEEP ME ENTERTAINED!

FLING!

PLOP!

WELL, MONKEY, YOU'RE BORED BECAUSE YOU BANISHED EVERYONE, SO NOW THERE'S NO ONE LEFT FOR YOU TO ANNOY.

CLICK!

SIGH! FINE! BRING THEM BACK!

AND TAKE THESE FLAGS DOWN, THEY'RE VERY SHOWY.

FINE! FINE!

RIP!

A FEW CHANGES LATER...

THERE! EVERYTHING'S BACK TO HOW IT WAS.

NOW WHAT?

NOW TAKE THIS SQUEAKY HAMMER...

...AND MAY YOU NEVER BE CURSED WITH INTELLIGENCE AGAIN!

SQUEAK-OO

163

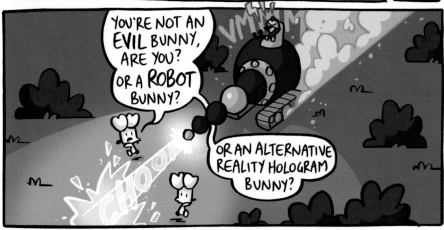

166

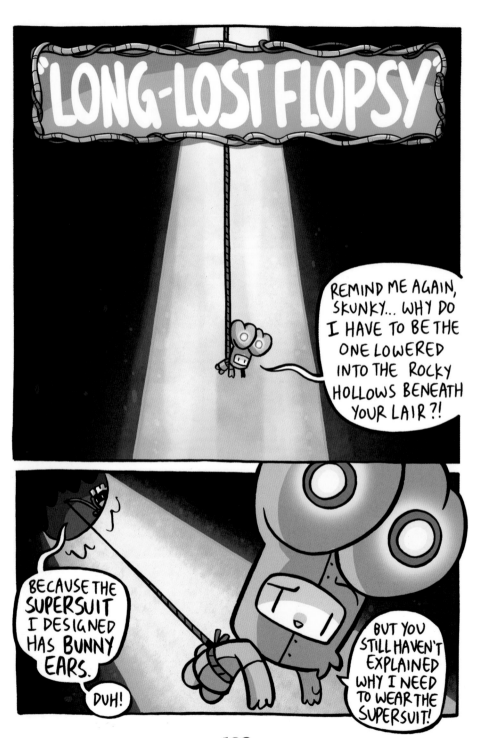

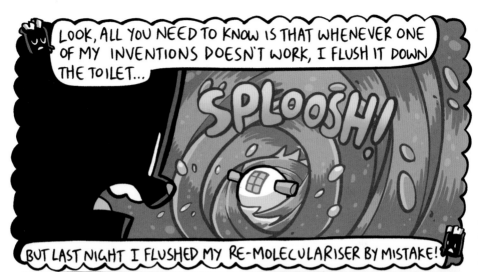

LOOK, ALL YOU NEED TO KNOW IS THAT WHENEVER ONE OF MY INVENTIONS DOESN'T WORK, I FLUSH IT DOWN THE TOILET...

SPLOOSH!

BUT LAST NIGHT I FLUSHED MY RE-MOLECULARISER BY MISTAKE!

WAIT, SO YOU WANT ME TO FISH THROUGH YOUR SEWAGE?

WELL, I WOULDN'T PHRASE IT LIKE THAT.

BECAUSE THEN YOU WOULDN'T DO IT.

FINE.

FINE!

SOONER I GET THIS DONE, SOONER I CAN GET BACK OUT.

169

"THE IMPOSSIBLE PIG"

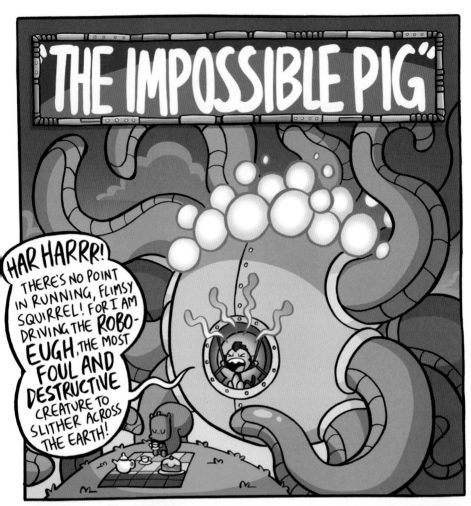

NOPE! I'M NOT HAVING IT. I'VE SPENT MY WHOLE LIFE BEING SCARED, BUT TODAY I WOKE UP AND DECIDED TO BE **BRAVE.**

BUT THAT'S NOT FAIR!

SIGH. COME DOWN HERE. I'LL SHOW WEENIE WHAT FEAR LOOKS LIKE.

HIGHLY COMBUSTIBLE SELF-DESTRUCT

BOOP!

WAIT! N—

KA-

BOOM!

175

I USED TO BE AT ONE WITH THE UNIVERSE...

I TOLD THE SUN WHEN TO RISE, THE EARTH TO TURN, THE TIDES TO EBB AND FLOW...

BUT LOOK AT ME NOW! I'M JUST A **PIG** WITH A **BEARD** ON A CLOUD.

PUTT PUTT!

177

MEANWHILE...

SKUNKY, I DON'T GET IT. WHY DID YOU BRING PIG BACK JUST TO LET HIM GET AWAY?

WELL...

THE ENTRAPMENT BEAM DIDN'T JUST HOLD PIG...

IT ABSORBED MOST OF HIS EXTRAORDINARY POWERS.

DOWNLOADING THEM ALL INTO THIS VAT OF GOOP! I PLAN TO SYNTHESISE HIS ABILITIES AND CREATE MY OWN.

ALL THAT POWER! AND IT'S OURS!

MINE.

WE WILL BE LIKE GODS!

SPLUT!!

CRASH!

OH, BOTTOMS.

180

SIGHHH.

HI, LUCKY! WHY ARE YOU HIDING IN A HEDGE?

SINCE PIG CAME BACK TO THE WOODS WITH A BEARD, HE'S BEEN ZAPPING THINGS, PINGING IN AND OUT OF PLACES.

IT'S HIS 'THING', Y'KNOW?

EVERYONE IN THESE WOODS HAS THEIR OWN THING. LIKE YOU, YOU'RE ALWAYS BAKING.

NOT ALWAYS.

IGNORE THIS.

ACTION BEAVER'S ALWAYS BLOWING HIMSELF UP.

NUZZLE -BLIPS!

BOOM!

AI'S SUPER FAST, LE FOX IS GRUMPY, EVE IS UNEMOTIONAL.

BAH!

CAN'T HEAR YOU! TOO FAST!

THIS IS ILLOGICAL. EVERYTHING'S SILLY.

183

184

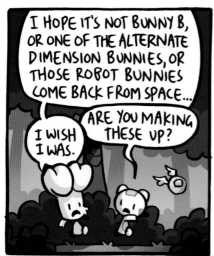

AND BEST OF ALL, THE CHAOS-O-TRON RUNS ON AN UNLIMITED SOURCE OF POWER...

...IT'S WIRED **DIRECTLY INTO ACTION BEAVER'S BRAIN!**

GNURP!

OH, THE **HUMANITY!**

I KNOW, RIGHT?

BUT YOU MUST HAVE BUILT A **SELF-DESTRUCT BUTTON** INTO IT, YOU ALWAYS DO!

YES, WHY **DO** YOU KEEP DOING THAT?

TO PREVENT YOU FROM TAKING MY BRILLIANT INVENTIONS AND BEING **SILLY** WITH THEM.

DUH.

HOWEVER, THIS TIME THE SELF-DESTRUCT BUTTON IS **REMOTE**.

I PUT IT ON A KEYCHAIN!

OOOOH.

HA HA!

ROOKIE MISTAKE!

SNATCH

PLLP!

WH... WHAT'S HAPPENING? I'M SLOWING DOWN!

THE CHAOS-O-TRON HAS TURNED YOU INTO TREACLE!

GIVE ME THE SELF-DESTRUCT BUTTON, I'LL PRESS IT!

GLOOP!

DUHH!

ME NOT SO SMART NO MORE.

WHAT DO WIV BUTTON?

191

"FENNEC FUN!"

UNCLE LE FOX, I'VE COME TO VISIT! THERE'LL BE SO MUCH NOISE, AND SO MUCH EXCITEMENT, IT'LL BE FUN!

SORRY, WHO ARE YOU?

I'M FENNEC, YOUR NIECE. AND I'M ON HALF TERM.

WELL, YOU CAN JUST GO HOME AGAIN. ZERE IS NO WAY I'M WASTING EVEN A MOMENT OF MY LIFE BABYSITTING YOU.

195

SUCH A THING IS NOT POSSIBLE. ZESE IDIOTS ARE DETERMINED TO MAKE MY LIFE AS MISERABLE AS ZEY CAN.

WELL, I THINK IT'S RUDE. HEY! YOU IN THE ROBOT!

ALL THIS BEAUTY YOU'RE SURROUNDED BY, ALL THIS FREEDOM, AND YOU WASTE YOUR TIME TEARING IT ALL UP!

YOU DON'T KNOW HOW LUCKY YOU ARE!

LOL! WHO'S THIS KID TRYING TO SPOIL OUR FUN?

MY NAME IS FENNEC. AND I BROKE MYSELF OUT OF A ZOO.

I LIKE HER.

YEAH, ME TOO.

MEANWHILE, AT THE ZOO...

HAR HAR! I'M FREE! AND I'VE HEARD UNCLE LE FOX HAS A PLACE TO STAY!

ARCTIC FOX

200

"BUTT THEN..."

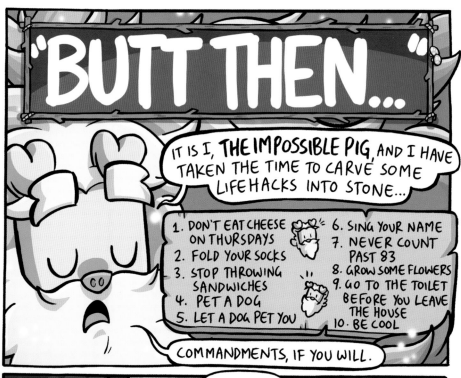

IT IS I, **THE IMPOSSIBLE PIG**, AND I HAVE TAKEN THE TIME TO CARVE SOME LIFEHACKS INTO STONE...

1. DON'T EAT CHEESE ON THURSDAYS
2. FOLD YOUR SOCKS
3. STOP THROWING SANDWICHES
4. PET A DOG
5. LET A DOG PET YOU
6. SING YOUR NAME
7. NEVER COUNT PAST 83
8. GROW SOME FLOWERS
9. GO TO THE TOILET BEFORE YOU LEAVE THE HOUSE
10. BE COOL

COMMANDMENTS, IF YOU WILL.

OOOOOOH!

THAT STUPID PIG. ACTING LIKE HE'S SO AMAZING.

WELL, I BET I COULD BRING HIM DOWN A PEG OR TWO.

DEVIOUS THOUGHTS

NEED MY HELP?

WELL, **DUHHH**, OBVIOUSLY.

NOT ONLY THAT, BUT THE POWER SUIT COMES PRE-INSTALLED WITH AN **EMBIGGENING** FUNCTION...

209

210

211

213

215

EVERY MARVEL, EVERY HORROR, EVERY HOLLOW AND FALL, EVERY TURN, COLLAPSE AND CLIMB.

EVERY SECRET...

OH. I FORGOT ABOUT THESE GUYS.

CHOMP CHOMP!

LE FOX! COME IN!

HAVE SOME PUNCH.

WE ARE JUST PASSING THROUGH.

BUT YOU'LL STAY FOR A GAME OF CHARADES!

NON.

ANGUS, DO JURASSIC PARK.

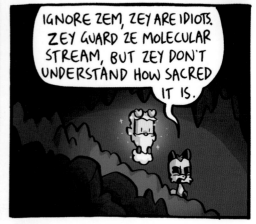

IGNORE ZEM, ZEY ARE IDIOTS. ZEY GUARD ZE MOLECULAR STREAM, BUT ZEY DON'T UNDERSTAND HOW SACRED IT IS.

BUT THE MOLECULAR STREAM IS EVERYWHERE, IT'S EVERY ATOM IN THE UNIVERSE, WHY WOULD THE ONLY WAY TO REACH IT BE DOWN HERE?

TSK.

ZE DARK EARTH PROVIDES US WITH A GATEWAY TO ZE STREAM. A BRIDGE FOR OUR FLESHY FORMS.

TO THOSE WHO UNDERSTAND ITS MAGIC, IT IS KNOWN AS..

...ZE LAKE OF ETERNITY!

OH.

I'M SURE IT USED TO BE DEEPER.

OH, SORRY, THAT'S US. WE'VE BEEN MIXING IT IN WITH THE PUNCH.

MAKES IT TINGLY!

NO MATTER. ZE **PUDDLE** OF ETERNITY IS STILL BIG ENOUGH FOR **ONE** TO PASS THROUGH.

THIS IS MY CHANCE.

FOR MY BODY TO SCATTER INTO BILLIONS OF ATOMS EVERYWHERE AND NOWHERE ALL AT ONCE!

THESE WOODS NEED NEVER THINK OF ME AGAIN.

PIG! NO!

BECAUSE IF I'M STUPID AGAIN, THEN I'LL FORGET ALL THIS.

AND I WON'T FEEL SO TERRIBLE.

YOU KNOW YOU'LL FORGET ALL ABOUT YOUR **INCREDIBLE POWERS** TOO?

I KNOW.

TRUNDLE TRUNDLE!

AND YOU KNOW ONE DAY I'LL WORK OUT HOW TO STEAL THEM FROM YOU?

I KNOW.

I KNOW.

I DON'T WANT THEM ANY MORE.

IDIFIER OOTH

ST... IFIER TH

225

HOW TO DRAW LUCKY

①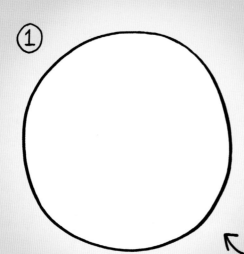

LUCKY MAY LOOK A LITTLE MORE DETAILED THAN THE OTHER CHARACTERS IN THE WOODS, BUT HER HEAD STARTS OUT AS A **GREAT BIG CIRCLE!**

②

AS EVER, ADDING A CROSS IN PENCIL (SO WE CAN RUB IT OUT LATER) HELPS US TO WORK OUT WHICH DIRECTION LUCKY WILL BE LOOKING.

③

FOR EXAMPLE, NOW WE CAN ADD HER **EYES** ALONG THAT HORIZONTAL LINE.

④

... AND WE CAN DRAW A LITTLE **NOSE** WHERE THE TWO LINES CROSS.

⑤

LUCKY HAS A **SNOUT**, WHICH CURVES AROUND HER NOSE...

⑥

...ONLY TO JOIN ONTO HER **MOUTH**!

⑦

ADD A COUPLE OF POINTY **TEETH**, AND A **TONGUE**!

⑧

EARS! LUCKY'S EARS ARE LIKE PLUMP TRIANGLES, WITH A LITTLE TUFT OF HAIR IN THE MIDDLE.

⑨

LET'S NOT FORGET THE OTHER TUFTS...ONE ON THE TOP, ONE EITHER SIDE OF HER CHEEKS!

① LUCKY'S BODY IS A **CURVED LUMP** BELOW HER HEAD.

②  FOR **ARMS**, WE CAN DRAW SAUSAGE SHAPES AND JUST ADD A FEW FINGERS AT EACH END!

③ LUCKY'S **FEET** ARE CIRCLES - LET'S DRAW HER JUMPING OFF THE GROUND!

(ADD A LITTLE LINE FOR THE SHADOW UNDERNEATH HER)

④ 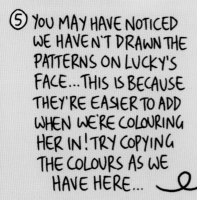 DON'T FORGET HER **TAIL**. IT'S ANOTHER SAUSAGE, THIS TIME WITH STRIPES!

⑤ YOU MAY HAVE NOTICED WE HAVEN'T DRAWN THE PATTERNS ON LUCKY'S FACE...THIS IS BECAUSE THEY'RE EASIER TO ADD WHEN WE'RE COLOURING HER IN! TRY COPYING THE COLOURS AS WE HAVE HERE...

AND WE'RE DONE! WHY NOT EXPERIMENT WITH DIFFERENT MOODS FOR LUCKY...LIKE EXCITED, SCARED, BRAVE, HEROIC, SLEEPING, SURPRISED...

WANT MORE FROM JAMIE SMART?

The Phoenix is the most **EXCITING** weekly comic in the UK! Every issue is packed full of **AMAZING STORIES** and inspirational **HOW-TO-DRAW GUIDES!**

SPECIAL PREVIEW!

The Phoenix is the only place you can read the NEWEST *Megalomaniacs!*

THE PHOENIX
GREAT STORIES EVERY WEEK

THE SKILLS HUB

DRAW YOUR MONSTERS

With Zak Simmonds-Hurn

WE'RE LEARNING HOW TO DRAW MONSTER PARTS, SO WE CAN BUILD OUR OWN MONSTER!

EYES, TEETH AND FANGS

MONSTROUS EYEBALLS

LET'S MAKE THOSE PEEPERS INTO CREEPERS!

JUST START WITH CIRCLES! ONE FOR THE EYEBALL, ONE FOR THE IRIS, ONE FOR THE PUPIL, LIKE THIS.

TO ADD SOME SHINE, LEAVE A SMALL WHITE CIRCLE IN THE PUPIL AND A CURVED RECTANGLE OVERLAPPING PART OF THE IRIS.

TO MAKE AN EYE-BALL LOOK VEINY, DRAW THIN, WIGGLY, BRANCHING LINES AROUND THE EDGE OF THE EYE.

YOU COULD PUT YOUR EYES ON STALKS FOR A REALLY STRANGE LOOK! JUST IMAGINE THERE'S A HOSEPIPE COMING OUT OF THE BACK OF THE EYE, CONNECTING IT TO YOUR MONSTER'S HEAD!

CREATURE FEATURES

LET'S GIVE YOUR TEETH AND EYES A HOME!

I STARTED WITH A VERY SIMPLE OUTLINE FOR THE MONSTER'S HEAD AND DREW A CIRCLE FOR THE EYE AND A BIG MOUTH SHAPE.

I DREW A PUPIL ON THE EYEBALL AND THEN ADDED SOME TEETH IN THE MOUTH. I DREW THEM NARROWER AND CLOSER AT EITHER SIDE OF THE MOUTH TO SHOW THAT THE TEETH CURVE AROUND IN A 'U' SHAPE.

LASTLY, I FILLED IN THE REST OF THE MOUTH - EVERYTHING THAT ISN'T TEETH!

TRY DIFFERENT TYPES OF EYES WITH DIFFERENT TYPES OF TEETH. THERE ARE SO MANY POSSIBILITIES, SO HAVE FUN PLAYING AROUND!

PROFESSOR BRAYN'S MONSTER TIPS!

MANY THINGS WILL AFFECT HOW YOU DESIGN YOUR MONSTER. HERE ARE SOME THINGS TO CONSIDER BEFORE YOU BEGIN.

BIG CHUNKY ROUNDED TEETH AND SIMPLE EYES MAKE YOUR MONSTER LOOK LESS THREATENING.

LOTS OF SHARP TEETH AND WEIRD EYES WILL GIVE YOUR MONSTER THE SCARE-FACTOR!

BUILDING OUR MONSTER:

HMM, IT CAN SEE ME, AND HAS A MOUTH NOW...

...IS IT JUST ME OR DOES IT LOOK HUNGRY?!

We've just learnt to draw eyes and mouths! Let's add those to a monster!

Learn how to draw horns, tails and much more in *The Phoenix*!

There are more PRO DRAWING TIPS just like this, every week in *The Phoenix*!

SPECIAL PREVIEW!

Find brand-new SHORTS and hilarious comics in *The Phoenix*!

Wasn't that AWESOME?! This is just a tiny glimpse!

DRAGON GUARD

FORGED IN *STAR-FIRE* AND UNITED BY *VALOUR*, THE DRAGON GUARD MUST DEFEND THE *ELDER DRAGON EGG*, HIDDEN IN THE HEART OF OUR SUN, AGAINST THE *FORCES OF EVIL*.

ART BY ZAK SIMMONDS-HURN — STORY BY TEAM PHOENIX

SOMEWHERE ON THE EDGE OF OUR SOLAR SYSTEM...

SHHIING!

KLANG!

SHING!

KRUNCH

BOOM

TAKE THAT, TITANITE SCUM!

KROOM!

MS ISABELLE, MORE OF THEM ARE ON THE WAY!

TO BE CONTINUED! Every issue of *The Phoenix* features EXCITING new episodes of ongoing stories!

JAMIE SMART HAS BEEN CREATING CHILDREN'S COMICS
FOR MANY YEARS, WITH POPULAR TITLES INCLUDING
BUNNY VS MONKEY, *LOOSHKIN*, *MAX AND CHAFFY*
FOR YOUNGER READERS, AND *FISH-HEAD STEVE*,
WHICH BECAME THE FIRST WORK OF ITS KIND TO BE
SHORTLISTED FOR THE ROALD DAHL FUNNY PRIZE.

THE FIRST FOUR BOOKS IN HIS *FLEMBER* SERIES
OF ILLUSTRATED NOVELS ARE AVAILABLE NOW.
HE ALSO WORKS ON MULTIMEDIA PROJECTS
LIKE *FIND CHAFFY*.

JAMIE LIVES IN THE SOUTH-EAST OF ENGLAND,
WHERE HE SPENDS HIS TIME THINKING UP STORIES
AND GETTING LOST ON DOG WALKS.